Art Fein

THE ADVENTURES OF THE BLACK GIRL
IN HER SEARCH FOR GOD

THE ADVENTURES OF
THE BLACK GIRL IN HER
SEARCH FOR GOD

GEORGE BERNARD SHAW

THE ADVENTURES OF
THE BLACK GIRL IN HER
SEARCH FOR GOD

With the original illustrations by
JOHN FARLEIGH

CAPRICORN BOOKS • NEW YORK

Library of Congress Catalogue
Card Number: 59-11379

MANUFACTURED IN THE UNITED STATES OF AMERICA

THE ADVENTURES OF THE BLACK GIRL
IN HER SEARCH FOR GOD

"WHERE is God?" said the black girl to the missionary who had converted her.

"He has said 'Seek and ye shall find Me'" said the missionary.

The missionary was a small white woman, not yet thirty: an odd little body who had found no satisfaction for her soul with her very respectable and fairly well-to-do family in her native England, and had settled down in the African forest to teach little African children to love Christ and adore the Cross. She was a born apostle of love. At school she had adored one or other of her teachers with an idolatry that was proof against all snubbing, but had never cared much for girls of her own age and standing. At eighteen she began falling in love with earnest clergymen, and actually became engaged to six of them in succession. But when it came to the point she always broke it off; for these love affairs, full at first of ecstatic happiness and hope, somehow became unreal and eluded her in the end. The clergymen thus suddenly and unaccountably disengaged did not always conceal their sense of relief and escape, as if they too had discovered that the dream was only a dream, or a sort of metaphor by which they had striven to express the real thing, but not itself the real thing.

One of the jilted, however, committed suicide; and this

7

tragedy gave her an extraordinary joy. It seemed to take her from a fool's paradise of false happiness into a real region in which intense suffering became transcendent rapture.

But it put an end to her queer marriage engagements. Not that it was the last of them. But a worldly cousin, of whose wit she was a little afraid, and who roundly called her a coquette and a jilt, one day accused her of playing in her later engagements for another suicide, and told her that many a woman had been hanged for less. And though she knew in a way that this was not true, and that the cousin, being a woman of this world, did not understand; yet she knew also that in the worldly way it was true enough, and that she must give up this strange game of seducing men into engagements which she now knew she would never keep. So she jilted the sixth clergyman and went to plant the cross in darkest Africa; and the last stirring in her of what she repudiated as sin was a flash of rage when he married the cousin, through whose wit and worldly wisdom he at last became a bishop in spite of himself.

The black girl, a fine creature, whose satin skin and shining muscles made the white missionary folk seem like ashen ghosts by contrast, was an interesting but unsatisfactory convert; for instead of taking Christianity with sweet docility exactly as it was administered to her, she met it with unexpected interrogative reactions which forced her teacher to improvise doctrinal replies and invent evidence on the spur of the moment to such an extent that at last she could not conceal from herself that the life of Christ, as she narrated it, had accreted so many circumstantial details and such a body of home-made doctrine that the Evangelists would have been amazed and confounded if they had been alive to hear it all put forward on their authority. Indeed the missionary's choice of a specially remote station, which had been at first an act of devotion, very soon became a necessity, as the appearance of a rival missionary would have led to the discovery that though some of the finest plums in the gospel pudding concocted by her had been picked out of the Bible, and the scenery and *dramatis personæ* borrowed from it, yet the resultant religion was, in spite of this element of compilation, really a product of the missionary's own direct inspiration. Only as a solitary pioneer missionary could she be her own Church and determine its canon without fear of being excommunicated as a heretic.

But she was perhaps rash when, having taught the black girl to read, she gave her a Bible on her birthday. For when the black girl, receiving her teacher's reply very literally, took her knobkerry and strode right off into the African forest in search of God, she took the Bible with her as her guidebook.

The first thing she met was a mamba snake, one of the few poisonous snakes that will attack mankind if crossed. Now the missionary, who was fond of making pets of animals because they were affectionate and never asked questions, had taught the black girl never to kill anything if she could help it, and never to be afraid of anything. So she grasped her knobkerry a little tighter and said to the mamba "I wonder who made you, and why he gave you the will to kill me and the venom to do it with."

The mamba immediately beckoned her by a twist of its head

to follow it, and led her to a pile of rocks on which sat enthroned a well-built aristocratic looking white man with handsome regular features, an imposing beard and luxuriant wavy hair, both as white as isinglass, and a ruthlessly severe expression. He had in his hand a staff which seemed a combination of sceptre, big stick, and great assegai; and with this he immediately killed the mamba, who was approaching him humbly and adoringly.

The black girl, having been taught to fear nothing, felt her heart harden against him, partly because she thought strong men ought to be black, and only missionary ladies white, partly because he had killed her friend the snake, and partly because he wore a ridiculous white nightshirt, and thereby rubbed her up on the one point on which her teacher had never been able to convert her, which was the duty of being ashamed of her person and wearing petticoats. There was a certain contempt in her voice as she addressed him.

"I am seeking God" she said. "Can you direct me?"

"You have found him" he replied. "Kneel down and worship me this very instant, you presumptuous creature, or dread my wrath. I am the Lord of Hosts: I made the heavens and the earth and all that in them is. I made the poison of the snake and the milk in your mother's breast. In my hand are death and all the diseases, the thunder and lightning, the storm and the pestilence, and all the other proofs of my greatness and majesty. On your knees, girl; and when you next come before me, bring me your favorite child and slay it here before me as a sacrifice; for I love the smell of newly spilled blood."

"I have no child" said the black girl. "I am a virgin."

"Then fetch your father and let him slay you" said the Lord of Hosts. "And see that your relatives bring me plenty of rams and goats and sheep to roast before me as offerings to propitiate me, or I shall certainly smite them with the most horrible plagues so that they may know that I am God."

"I am not a piccaninny, nor even a grown up ninny, to believe such wicked nonsense" said the black girl; "and in the name of the true God whom I seek I will scotch you as you scotched that poor mamba." And she bounded up the rocks at him, brandishing her knobkerry.

But when she reached the top there was nothing there. This so bewildered her that she sat down and took out her Bible for guidance. But whether the ants had got at it, or, being a very old book, it had perished by natural decay, all the early pages had crumbled to dust which blew away when she opened it.

So she sighed and got up and resumed her search. Presently she disturbed a rattlesnake or ringhals, which was gliding away when she said "Well, Clicky-clicky: you are not so ill-natured as the mamba. You give warning and go quietly about your business if we go quietly about ours. Your God must be nicer than the mamba's God."

On that, the rattlesnake came back and beckoned her to follow him, which she did.

He led her to a pleasant glade in which an oldish gentleman with a soft silvery beard and hair, also in a white nightshirt, was sitting at a table covered with a white cloth and strewn with manuscript poems and pens made of angels' quills. He looked kindly enough; but his turned up moustaches and eyebrows expressed a self-satisfied cunning which the black girl thought silly.

"Good little Clicky-clicky" he said to the snake. "You have brought somebody to argue with me." And he gave the snake an egg, which it carried away joyfully into the forest.

"Do not be afraid of me" he said to the black girl. "I am not a cruel god: I am a reasonable one. I do nothing worse than argue. I am a Nailer at arguing. Dont worship me. Reproach me. Find fault with me. Dont spare my feelings. Throw something in my teeth; so that I can argue about it."

"Did you make the world?" said the black girl.

"Of course I did" he said.

"Why did you make it with so much evil in it?" she said.

"Splendid!" said the god. "That is just what I wanted you to ask me. You are a clever intelligent girl. I had a servant named Job once to argue with; but he was so modest and stupid that I had to shower the most frightful misfortunes on him before I could provoke him to complain. His wife told him to curse me and die; and I dont wonder at the poor woman; for I gave him a terrible time, though I made it all up to him afterwards. When at last I got him arguing, he thought a lot of himself. But I soon shewed him up. He acknowledged that I had the better of him. I took him down handsomely, I tell you."

"I do not want to argue" said the black girl. "I want to know why, if you really made the world, you made it so badly."

"Badly!" cried the Nailer. "Ho! You set yourself up to call me to account! Who are you, pray, that you should criticize me?

Can you make a better world yourself? Just try: that's all. Try to make one little bit of it. For instance, make a whale. Put a hook in its nose and bring it to me when you have finished. Do you realize, you ridiculous little insect, that I not only made the whale, but made the sea for him to swim in? The whole mighty ocean, down to its bottomless depths and up to the top of the skies. You think that was easy, I suppose. You think you could do it better yourself. I tell you what, young woman: you want the conceit taken out of you. You couldnt make a mouse; and you set yourself up against me, who made a megatherium. You couldnt make a pond; and you dare talk to me, the maker of the seven seas. You will be ugly and old and dead in fifty years, whilst my majesty will endure for ever; and here you are taking me to task as if you were my aunt. You think, dont you, that you are better than God? What have you to say to that argument?"

"It isnt an argument: it's a sneer" said the black girl. "You dont seem to know what an argument is."

"What! I who put down Job, as all the world admits, not know what an argument is! I simply laugh at you, child" said the old gentleman, considerably huffed, but too astonished to take the situation in fully.

"I dont mind your laughing at me" said the black girl; "but you have not told me why you did not make the world all good instead of a mixture of good and bad. It is no answer to ask me whether I could have made it any better myself. If I were God there would be no tsetse flies. My people would not fall down in fits and have dreadful swellings and commit sins. Why did you put a bag of poison in the mamba's mouth when other snakes can live as well without it? Why did you make the monkeys so ugly and the birds so pretty?"

"Why shouldnt I?" said the old gentleman. "Answer me that."

"Why should you? unless you have a taste for mischief" said the black girl.

"Asking conundrums is not arguing" he said. "It is not playing the game."

"A God who cannot answer my questions is no use to me" said the black girl. "Besides, if you had really made everything you would know why you made the whale as ugly as he is in the pictures."

"If I chose to amuse myself by making him look funny, what is that to you?" he said. "Who are you to dictate to me how I shall make things?"

"I am tired of you" said the black girl. "You always come back to the same bad manners. I dont believe you ever made anything. Job must have been very stupid not to find you out. There are too many old men pretending to be gods in this forest."

She sprang at him with her knobkerry uplifted; but he dived nimbly under the table, which she thought must have sunk into the earth; for when she reached it there was nothing there. And when she resorted to her Bible again the wind snatched thirty more pages out of it and scattered them in dust over the trees.

After this adventure the black girl felt distinctly sulky. She had not found God; her Bible was half spoilt; and she had lost her temper twice without any satisfaction whatever. She began

to ask herself whether she had not overrated white beards and old age and nightshirts as divine credentials. It was lucky that this was her mood when she came upon a remarkably good looking clean shaven white young man in a Greek tunic. She had never seen anything like him before. In particular there was a lift and twist about the outer corners of his brows that both interested and repelled her.

"Excuse me, baas," she said. "You have knowing eyes. I am in search of God. Can you direct me?"

"Do not trouble about that" said the young man. "Take the world as it comes; for beyond it there is nothing. All roads end at the grave, which is the gate of nothingness; and in the shadow of nothingness everything is vanity. Take my advice and seek no further than the end of your nose. You will always know that there is something beyond that; and in that knowledge you will be hopeful and happy."

"My mind ranges further" said the black girl. "It is not right to shut one's eyes. I desire knowledge of God more than happiness or hope. God is my happiness and my hope."

"How if you find that there is no God?" said the young man.

"I should be a bad woman if I did not know that God exists" said the black girl.

"Who told you that?" said the young man. "You should not let people tie up your mind with such limitations. Besides, why should you not be a bad woman?"

"That is nonsense" said the black girl. "Being a bad woman means being something you ought not to be."

"Then you must find out what you ought to be before you can tell whether you are a good woman or a bad one."

"That is true" said the black girl. "But I know I ought to be a good woman even if it is bad to be good."

"There is no sense in that" said the young man.

"Not your sort of sense but God's sort of sense" she said. "I want to have that sort of sense; and I feel that when I have got it I shall be able to find God."

"How can you tell what you shall find?" he said. "My counsel to you is to do all the work that comes to you as well as you can while you can, and so fill up with use and honor the days that remain to you before the inevitable end, when there will be neither counsel nor work, neither doing nor knowing, nor even being."

"There will be a future when I am dead" said the black girl. "If I cannot live it I can know it."

"Do you know the past?" said the young man. "If the past, which has really happened, is beyond your knowledge, how can you hope to know the future, which has not yet happened?"

"Yet it will happen; and I know enough of it to tell you that the sun will rise every day" said the black girl.

"That also is vanity" said the young sage. "The sun is burning and must some day burn itself out."

"Life is a flame that is always burning itself out; but it catches fire again every time a child is born. Life is greater than death, and hope than despair. I will do the work that comes to me only if I know that it is good work; and to know that, I must know the past and the future, and must know God."

"You mean that you must *be* God" he said, looking hard at her.

"As much as I can" said the black girl. "Thank you. We who are young are the wise ones: I have learned from you that to know God is to be God. You have strengthened my soul. Before I leave you, tell me who you are."

"I am Koheleth, known to many as Ecclesiastes the preacher" he replied. "God be with you if you can find him! He is not with me. Learn Greek: it is the language of wisdom. Farewell."

He made a friendly sign and passed on. The black girl went the opposite way, thinking harder than ever; but the train of thought he had started in her became so puzzling and difficult that at last she fell asleep and walked steadily on in her sleep until she smelt a lion, and, waking suddenly, saw him sitting in the middle of her path, sunning himself like a cat before the hearth: a lion of the kind they call maneless because its mane is handsome and orderly and not like a touzled mop.

"In God's name, Dicky" she said, giving his throat as she passed him a caressing little pull with her fingers which felt as if she had pulled at a warm tuft of moss on a mountain.

King Richard beamed graciously, and followed her with his eyes as if he had an impulse to go for a walk with her; but she left him too decisively for that; and she, remembering that there are many less amiable and even stronger creatures in the forest than he, proceeded more warily until she met a dark man with wavy black hair, and a number six nose. He had nothing on but a pair of sandals. His face was very much wrinkled; but the wrinkles were those of pity and kindliness, though the number six nose had large courageous nostrils, and the corners of his mouth were resolute. She heard him before she saw him; for he

was making strange roaring and hooting noises and seemed in great trouble. When he saw her he stopped roaring and tried to look ordinary and unconcerned.

"Say, baas" said the black girl: "are you the prophet that goes stripped and naked, wailing like the dragons and mourning like the owls?"

"I do a little in that line" he said apologetically. "Micah is my name: Micah the Morasthite. Can I do anything for you?"

"I seek God" she answered.

"And have you found Him?" said Micah.

"I found an old man who wanted me to roast animals for him because he loved the smell of cooking, and to sacrifice my children on his altar."

At this Micah uttered such a lamentable roar that King Richard hastily took cover in the forest and sat watching there with his tail slashing.

"He is an impostor and a horror" roared Micah. "Can you see yourself coming before the high God with burnt calves of a year old? Would He be pleased with thousands of rams or rivers of oil or the sacrifice of your first born, the fruit of your body, instead of the devotion of your soul? God has shewed your soul what is good; and your soul has told you that He speaks the truth. And what does He require of you but to do justice and love mercy and walk humbly with Him?"

"This is a third God" she said; "and I like him much better than the one who wanted sacrifices and the one who wanted me to argue with him so that he might sneer at my weakness and ignorance. But doing justice and shewing mercy is only a small part of life when one is not a baas or a judge. And what is the use of walking humbly if you dont know where you are walking to?"

"Walk humbly and God will guide you" said the Prophet. "What is it to you whither He is leading you?"

"He gave me eyes to guide myself" said the black girl. "He gave me a mind and left me to use it. How can I now turn on Him and tell Him to see for me and to think for me?"

Micah's only reply was such a fearful roar that King Richard fairly bolted and ran for two miles without stopping. And the black girl did the same in the opposite direction. But she ran only a mile.

"What am I running away from?" she said to herself, pulling herself up. "I'm not afraid of that dear noisy old man."

"Your fears and hopes are only fancies" said a voice close to her, proceeding from a very shortsighted elderly man in spectacles who was sitting on a gnarled log. "In running away you were acting on a conditioned reflex. It is quite simple. Having lived among lions you have from your childhood associated the sound of a roar with deadly danger. Hence your precipitate flight when that superstitious old jackass brayed at you. This remarkable discovery cost me twenty-five years of devoted research, during which I cut out the brains of innumerable dogs, and observed their spittle by making holes in their cheeks for them to salivate through instead of through their tongues. The whole scientific world is prostrate at my feet in admiration of this colossal achievement and gratitude for the light it has shed on the great problems of human conduct."

"Why didnt you ask me?" said the black girl. "I could have told you in twenty-five seconds without hurting those poor dogs."

"Your ignorance and presumption are unspeakable" said the old myop. "The fact was known of course to every child; but it had never been proved experimentally in the laboratory; and therefore it was not scientifically known at all. It reached me as an unskilled conjecture: I handed it on as science. Have you ever performed an experiment, may I ask?"

"Several" said the black girl. "I will perform one now. Do you know what you are sitting on?"

"I am sitting on a log grey with age, and covered with an uncomfortable rugged bark" said the myop.

"You are mistaken" said the black girl. "You are sitting on a sleeping crocodile."

With a yell which Micah himself might have envied, the myop rose and fled frantically to a neighboring tree, up which he climbed catlike with an agility which in so elderly a gentleman was quite superhuman.

"Come down" said the black girl. "You ought to know that crocodiles are only to be found near rivers. I was only trying an experiment. Come down."

"How am I to come down?" said the myop, trembling. "I should break my neck."

"How did you get up?" said the black girl.

"I dont know" he replied, almost in tears. "It is enough to make a man believe in miracles. I couldnt have climbed this tree; and yet here I am and shall never be able to get down again."

"A very interesting experiment, wasnt it?" said the black girl.

"A shamefully cruel one, you wicked girl" he moaned. "Pray did it occur to you that you might have killed me? Do you suppose you can give a delicate physiological organism like mine a violent shock without the most serious and quite possibly fatal reactions on the heart? I shall never be able to sit on a log again as long as I live. I believe my pulse is quite abnormal, though I cannot count it; for if I let go of this branch I shall drop like a stone."

"If you can cut half a dog's brain out without causing any reactions on its spittle you need not worry" she said calmly. "I think African magic much more powerful than your divining by dogs. By saying one word to you I made you climb a tree like a cat. You confess it was a miracle."

"I wish you would say another word and get me safely down again, confound you for a black witch" he grumbled.

"I will" said the black girl. "There is a tree snake smelling at the back of your neck."

The myop was on the ground in a jiffy. He landed finally on his back; but he scrambled to his feet at once and said "You did not take me in: dont think it. I knew perfectly well you were inventing that snake to frighten me."

"And yet you were as frightened as if it had been a real snake" said the black girl.

"I was not" said the myop indignantly. "I was not frightened in the least."

"You nipped down the tree as if you were" said the black girl.

"That is what is so interesting" said the myop, recovering his self-possession now that he felt safe. "It was a conditioned reflex.

I wonder could I make a dog climb a tree."

"What for?" said the black girl.

"Why, to place this phenomenon on a scientific basis" said he.

"Nonsense!" said the black girl. "A dog cant climb a tree."

"Neither can I without the stimulus of an imaginary crocodile" said the professor. "How am I to make a dog imagine a crocodile?"

"Introduce him to a few real ones to begin with" said the black girl.

"That would cost a good deal" said the myop, wrinkling his brows. "Dogs are cheap if you buy them from professional dog-stealers, or lay in a stock when the dog tax becomes due; but crocodiles would run into a lot of money. I must think this out carefully."

"Before you go" said the black girl "tell me whether you believe in God."

"God is an unnecessary and discarded hypothesis" said the myop. "The universe is only a gigantic system of reflexes produced by shocks. If I give you a clip on the knee you will wag your ankle."

"I will also give you a clip with my knobkerry; so dont do it" said the black girl.

"For scientific purposes it is necessary to inhibit such secondary and apparently irrelevant reflexes by tying the subject down" said the professor. "Yet they also are quite relevant as examples of reflexes produced by association of ideas. I have spent twenty-five years studying their effects."

"Effects on what?" said the black girl.

"On a dog's saliva" said the myop.

"Are you any the wiser?" she said.

"I am not interested in wisdom" he replied: "in fact I do not know what it means and have no reason to believe that it exists. My business is to learn something that was not known before. I impart that knowledge to the world, and thereby add to the body of ascertained scientific truth."

"How much better will the world be when it is all knowledge and no mercy?" said the black girl. "Havnt you brains enough to invent some decent way of finding out what you want to know?"

"Brains!" cried the myop, as if he could hardly believe his ears. "You must be an extraordinarily ignorant young woman. Do you not know that men of science are all brains from head to foot?"

"Tell that to the crocodile" said the black girl. "And tell me this. Have you ever considered the effect of your experiments on other people's minds and characters? Is it worth while losing your own soul and damning everybody else's to find out something about a dog's spittle?"

"You are using words that have no meaning" said the myop. "Can you demonstrate the existence of the organ you call a soul on the operating table or in the dissecting room? Can you reproduce the operation you call damning in the laboratory?"

"I can turn a live body with a soul into a dead one without it with a whack of my knobkerry" said the black girl "and you will soon see the difference and smell it. When people damn their souls by doing something wicked, you soon see the difference too."

"I have seen a man die: I have never seen one damn his soul" said the myop.

"But you have seen him go to the dogs" said the black girl. "You have gone to the dogs yourself, havnt you?"

"A quip; and an extremely personal one" said the myop haughtily. "I leave you."

So he went his way trying to think of some means of making a dog climb a tree in order to prove scientifically that he himself could climb one; and the black girl went her opposite way until she came to a hill on the top of which stood a huge cross guarded by a Roman soldier with a spear. Now in spite of all the teachings of the missionary, who found in the horrors of the crucifixion the same strange joy she had found in breaking her own heart and those of her lovers, the black girl hated the cross and thought it a great pity that Jesus had not died peacefully and painlessly and naturally, full of years and wisdom, protecting his granddaughters (her imagination always completed the picture with at least twenty promising black granddaughters) against the selfishness and violence of their parents. So she was averting her head from the cross with an expression of disgust when the Roman soldier sprang at her with his spear at the charge and shouted fiercely "On your knees, blackamoor, before the instrument and symbol of Roman justice, Roman law, Roman order and Roman peace."

But the black girl side-stepped the spear and swung her knobkerry so heartily on to the nape of his neck that he went down

SPQR

JUDGE NOT THAT YE
BE NOT JUDGED

sprawling and trying vainly to co-ordinate the movement of his legs sufficiently to rise. "That is the blackamoor instrument and symbol of all those fine things" said the black girl, shewing him the knobkerry. "How do you like it?"

"Hell!" groaned the soldier. "The tenth legion rabbit-punched by a black bitch! This is the end of the world." And he ceased struggling and lay down and cried like a child.

He recovered before she had gone very far; but being a Roman soldier he could not leave his post to gratify his feelings. The last she saw of him before the brow of the hill cut off their view of one another was the shaking of his fist at her; and the last she heard from him need not be repeated here.

Her next adventure was at a well where she stopped to drink, and suddenly saw a man whom she had not noticed before sitting beside it. As she was about to scoop up some water in her hand he produced a cup from nowhere and said

"Take this and drink in remembrance of me."

"Thank you, baas" she said, and drank. "Thank you kindly."

She gave him back the cup; and he made it disappear like a conjurer, at which she laughed and he laughed too.

"That was clever, baas" she said. "Great magician, you. You perhaps tell black woman something. I am in search of God. Where is He?"

"Within you" said the conjurer. "Within me too."

"I think so" said the girl. "But what is He?"

"Our father" said the conjurer.

The black girl made a wry face and thought for a moment. "Why not our mother?" she said then.

It was the conjurer's turn to make a wry face; and he made it. "Our mothers would have us put them before God," he said. "If I had been guided by my mother I should perhaps have been a rich man instead of an outcast and a wanderer; but I should not have found God."

"My father beat me from the time I was little until I was big enough to lay him out with my knobkerry" said the black girl; "and even after that he tried to sell me to a white baas-soldier who had left his wife across the seas. I have always refused to say 'Our father which art in heaven.' I always say 'Our grandfather.' I will not have a God who is my father."

"That need not prevent us loving one another like brother and sister" said the conjurer smiling; for the grandfather amendment tickled his sense of humor. Besides, he was a goodnatured fellow who smiled whenever he could.

"A woman does not love her brother" said the black girl. "Her heart turns from her brother to a stranger as my heart turns to you."

"Well: let us drop the family: it is only a metaphor" said the conjurer. "We are members of the same body of mankind, and therefore members one of another. Let us leave it at that."

"I cannot, baas," she said. "God tells me that He has nothing to do with bodies, and fathers and mothers, and sisters and brothers."

"It is a way of saying love one another: that is all" said the conjurer. "Love them that hate you. Bless them that curse you. Never forget that two blacks do not make a white."

"I do not want everyone to love me" said the black girl. "I

cannot love everybody. I do not want to. God tells me that I must not hit people with my knobkerry merely because I dislike them, and that their dislike of me—if they happen to dislike me —gives them no right to hit me. But God makes me dislike many people. And there are people who must be killed like snakes, because they rob and kill other people."

"I wish you would not remind me of these people" said the conjurer. "They make me very unhappy."

"It makes things very nice to forget about the unpleasant things" said the black girl; "but it does not make them believable; and it does not make them right. Do you really and truly love me, baas?"

The conjurer shrank, but immediately smiled kindly as he replied "Do not let us make a personal matter of it."

"But it has no sense if it is not a personal matter" said the black girl. "Suppose I tell you I love you, as you tell me I ought! Do you not feel that I am taking a liberty with you?"

"Certainly not" said the conjurer. "You must not think that. Though you are black and I am white we are equal before God who made us so."

"I am not thinking about that at all" said the black girl. "I forgot when I spoke that I am black and that you are only a poor white. Think of me as a white queen and of yourself as a white king. What is the matter? Why did you start?"

"Nothing. Nothing" said the conjurer. "Or—Well, I am the poorest of poor whites; yet I have thought of myself as a king. But that was when the wickedness of men had driven me crazy."

"I have seen worse kings" said the black girl; "so you need not blush. Well, let you be King Solomon and let me be Queen of Sheba, same as in the Bible. I come to you and say that I love you. That means I have come to take possession of you. I come with the love of a lioness and eat you up and make you a part of myself. From this time you will have to think, not of what pleases you, but of what pleases me. I will stand between you and yourself, between you and God. Is not that a terrible tyranny? Love is a devouring thing. Can you imagine heaven with love in it?"

"In my heaven there is nothing else. What else is heaven but love?" said the conjurer, boldly but uncomfortably.

"It is glory. It is the home of God and of his thoughts: there is no billing and cooing there, no clinging to one another like a tick to a sheep. The missionary, my teacher, talks of love; but she has run away from all her lovers to do God's work. The whites turn their eyes away from me lest they should love me. There are companies of men and women who have devoted themselves to God's work; but though they call themselves brotherhoods and sisterhoods they do not speak to one another."

"So much the worse for them" said the conjurer.

"It is silly, of course" said the black girl. "We have to live with people and must make the best of them. But does it not shew that our souls need solitude as much as our bodies need love? We need the help of one another's bodies and the help of one another's minds; but our souls need to be alone with God; and when people come loving you and wanting your soul as well as your mind and body, you cry 'Keep your distance: I belong to myself, not to you.' This 'love one another' of yours is worse mockery to me who am in search of God than it is to the warrior who must fight against murder and slavery, or the hunter who must slay or see his children starve."

"Shall I then say 'This commandment I give unto you: that you kill one another'?" said the conjurer.

"It is only the other one turned inside out" said the black girl. "Neither is a rule to live by. I tell you these cure-all commandments of yours are like the pills the cheap jacks sell us: they are useful once in twenty times perhaps, but in the other nineteen they are no use. Besides, I am not seeking commandments. I am seeking God."

"Continue your search; and God be with you" said the conjurer. "To find him, such as you must go past me." And with that he vanished.

"That is perhaps your best trick" said the black girl; "though I am sorry to lose you; for to my mind you are a lovable man and mean well."

A mile further on she met an ancient fisherman carrying an enormous cathedral on his shoulders.

"Take care: it will break your poor old back" she cried, running to help him.

"Not it" he replied cheerfully. "I am the rock on which this Church is built."

"But you are not a rock; and it is too heavy for you," she said, expecting every moment to see him crushed by its weight.

"No fear" he said, grinning pleasantly at her. "It is made entirely of paper." And he danced past her, making all the bells in the cathedral tinkle merrily.

Before he was out of sight several others, dressed in different costumes of black and white and all very carefully soaped and brushed, came along carrying smaller and mostly much uglier paper Churches. They all cried to her "Do not believe the fisherman. Do not listen to those other fellows. Mine is the true Church." At last she had to turn aside into the forest to avoid them; for they began throwing stones at one another; and as their aim was almost as bad as if they were blind, the stones came flying all over the road. So she concluded that she would not find God to her taste among them.

When they had passed, or rather when the battle had rolled by, she returned to the road, where she found a very old wandering Jew, who said to her "Has He come?"

"Has who come?" said the black girl.

"He who promised to come" said the Jew. "He who said that I must tarry 'til he comes. I have tarried beyond all reason. If He does not come soon now it will be too late; for men learn nothing except how to kill one another in greater and greater numbers."

"That wont be stopped by anybody coming" said the black girl.

"But He will come in glory, sitting on the right hand of God" cried the Jew. "He said so. He will set everything right."

"If you wait for other people to come and set everything right" said the black girl "you will wait for ever." At that the Jew uttered a wail of despair; spat at her; and tottered away.

She was by this time quite out of conceit with old men; so she was glad to shake him off. She marched on until she came to a shady bank by the wayside; and here she found fifty of her own

black people, evidently employed as bearers, sitting down to enjoy a meal at a respectful distance from a group of white gentlemen and ladies. As the ladies wore breeches and sunhelmets the black girl knew that they were explorers, like the men. They had just finished eating. Some of them were dozing: others were writing in note books.

"What expedition is this?" said the black girl to the leader of the bearers.

"It is called the Caravan of the Curious" he replied.

"Are they good whites or bad?" she asked.

"They are thoughtless, and waste much time quarreling about trifles" he said. "And they ask questions for the sake of asking questions."

"Hi! you there" cried one of the ladies. "Go about your business: you cannot stop here. You will upset the men."

"No more than you" said the black girl.

"Stuff, girl" said the lady: "I am fifty. I am a neuter. Theyre used to me. Get along with you."

"You need not fear: they are not white men" said the black girl rather contemptuously. "Why do you call yourselves the Caravan of the Curious? What are you curious about? Are you curious about God?"

There was such a hearty laugh at this that those who were having a nap woke up and had to have the joke repeated to them.

"Many hundred years have passed since there has been any curiosity on that subject in civilized countries" said one of the gentlemen.

"Not since the fifteenth century, I should say" said another. "Shakespear is already quite Godless."

"Shakespear was not everybody" said a third. "The national anthem belongs to the eighteenth century. In it you find us ordering God about to do our political dirty work."

"Not the same God" said the second gentleman. "In the middle ages God was conceived as ordering us about and keeping our noses to the grindstone. With the rise of the bourgeoisie and the shaking off by the feudal aristocracy of the duties that used to be the price of their privileges you get a new god, who is ordered about and has his nose kept to the grindstone by the upper classes. 'Confound their politics; frustrate their knavish tricks' and so forth."

"Yes," said the first gentleman; "and·also a third god of the petty bourgeoisie, whose job it is, when they have filled the recording angel's slate with their trade dishonesties for the week, to wipe the slate clean with his blood on Sunday."

"Both these gods are still going strong" said the third gentleman. "If you doubt it, try to provide a decent second verse for the national anthem; or to expunge the Atonement from the prayerbook."

"That makes six gods that I have met or heard of in my search; but none of them is the God I seek" said the black girl.

"Are you in search of God?" said the first gentleman. "Had you not better be content with Mumbo Jumbo, or whatever you call the god of your tribe? You will not find any of ours an improvement on him."

"We have a very miscellaneous collection of Mumbo Jumbos"

said the third gentleman, "and not one that we can honestly recommend to you."

"That may be so" said the black girl. "But you had better be careful. The missionaries teach us to believe in your gods. It is all the instruction we get. If we find out that you do not believe in them and are their enemies we may come and kill you. There are millions of us; and we can shoot as well as you."

"There is something in that" said the second gentleman. "We have no right to teach these people what we do not believe. They may take it in deadly earnest. Why not tell them the simple truth that the universe has occurred through Natural Selection, and that God is a fable."

"It would throw them back on the doctrine of the survival of the fittest" said the first gentleman dubiously; "and it is not clear that we are the fittest to survive in competition with them. That girl is a fine specimen. We have had to give up employing poor whites for the work of our expedition: the natives are stronger, cleaner, and more intelligent."

"Besides having much better manners" said one of the ladies.

"Precisely" said the first gentleman. "I should really prefer to teach them to believe in a god who would give us a chance against them if they started a crusade against European atheism."

"You cannot teach these people the truth about the universe" said a spectacled lady. "It is, we now know, a mathematical universe. Ask that girl to divide a quantity by the square root of minus x, and she will not have the faintest notion what you mean. Yet division by the square root of minus x is the key to the universe."

"A skeleton key" said the second gentleman. "To me the square root of minus x is flat nonsense. Natural Selection—"

"What is the use of all this?" groaned a depressed gentleman. "The one thing we know for certain is that the sun is losing its heat, and that we shall presently die of cold. What does anything matter in the face of that fact?"

"Cheer up, Mr Croker" said a lively young gentleman. "As chief physicist to this expedition I am in a position to inform you authoritatively that unless you reject the undoubted fact of cosmic radiation you have just as much reason to believe that the sun is getting hotter and hotter and will eventually cremate us all alive."

"What comfort is there in that?" said Mr Croker. "We perish anyhow."

"Not necessarily" said the first gentleman.

"Yes, necessarily" said Mr Croker rudely. "The elements of temperature within which life can exist are ascertained and unquestionable. You cannot live at the temperature of frozen air and you cannot live at the temperature of a cremation furnace. No matter which of these temperatures the earth reaches we perish."

"Pooh!" said the first gentleman. "Our bodies, which are the only part of us to which your temperatures are fatal, will perish in a few years, mostly in well ventilated bedrooms kept at a quite comfortable temperature. But the something that makes the difference between the live body and the dead one: is there a rag of proof, a ray of probability even, that it is in any way dependent on temperature? It is certainly not flesh nor blood nor bone, though it has the curious property of building bodily organs for itself in those forms. It is incorporeal: if you try to figure it at all you must figure it as an electro-magnetic wave, as a rate of vibration, as a vortex in the ether if there be an ether: that is to say as something that, if it exists at all—and who can question its existence?—can exist on the coldest of the dead stars or in the hottest crater of the sun."

"Besides" said one of the ladies, "how do you know that the sun is hot?"

"You ask that in Africa!" said Mr Croker scornfully. "I feel it to be hot: that is how I know."

"You feel pepper to be hot" said the lady, returning his scorn with interest; "but you cannot light a match at it."

"You feel that a note at the right end of the piano keyboard is higher than a note at the left; yet they are both on the same level" said another lady.

"You feel that a macaw's coloring is loud; but it is really as soundless as a sparrow's," said yet another lady.

"You need not condescend to answer such quibbles" said an authoritative gentleman. "They are on the level of the three card trick. I am a surgeon; and I know, as a matter of observed fact, that the diameter of the vessels which supply blood to the female brain is excessive according to the standard set by the male brain. The resultant surcharge of blood both overstimulates and confuses the imagination, and so produces an iconosis in which the pungency of pepper suggests heat, the scream of a soprano height, and the flamboyancy of a macaw noise."

"Your literary style is admirable, Doctor" said the first gentleman; "but it is beside my point, which is that whether the sun's heat is the heat of pepper or the heat of flame, whether the moon's cold is the coldness of ice or the coldness of a snub to a poor relation, they are just as likely to be inhabited as the earth."

"The coldest parts of the earth are not inhabited" said Mr Croker.

"The hottest are" said the first gentleman. "And the coldest probably would be if there were not plenty of accommodation on earth for us in more congenial climates. Besides, there are Emperor penguins in the Antarctic. Why should there not be Emperor salamanders in the sun? Our great grandmothers, who believed in a brimstone hell, knew that the soul, as they called the thing that leaves the body when it dies and makes the difference between life and death, could live eternally in flames. In that they were much more scientific than my friend Croker here."

"A man who believes in hell could believe in anything" said Mr Croker, "even in the inheritance of acquired habits."

"I thought you believed in evolution, Croker" said a gentleman who was naturalist to the expedition.

"I *do* believe in evolution" said Mr Croker warmly. "Do you take me for a fundamentalist?"

"If you believe in evolution" said the naturalist "you must believe that all habits are both acquired and inherited. But you all have the Garden of Eden in your blood still. The way you fellows take in new ideas without ever thinking of throwing out the old ones makes you public dangers. You are all fundamentalists with a top dressing of science. That is why you are the stupidest of conservatives and reactionists in politics and the most bigoted of obstructionists in science itself. When it comes to getting a move on you are all of the same opinion: stop it, flog it, hang it, dynamite it, stamp it out."

"All of the same opinion!" exclaimed the first lady. "Have they ever agreed on any subject?"

"They are all looking in the same direction at present" said a lady with a sarcastic expression.

"What direction?" said the first lady.

"That direction" said the sarcastic lady, pointing to the black girl.

"Are you there still?" said the first lady. "You were told to go. Get along with you."

The black girl did not reply. She contemplated the lady gravely and let the knobkerry swing slowly between her fingers. Then she looked at the mathematical lady and said "Where does it grow?"

"Where does what grow?" said the mathematical lady.

"The root you spoke of" said the black girl. "The square root of Myna's sex."

"It grows in the mind" said the lady. "It is a number. Can you count forwards from one?"

"One, two, three, four, five, do you mean?" said the black girl, helping herself by her fingers.

"Just so" said the lady. "Now count backwards from one."

"One, one less, two less, three less, four less."

They all clapped their hands. "Splendid!" cried one. "Newton!" said another. "Leibniz!" said a third. "Einstein!" said a fourth. And then altogether, "Marvellous! marvellous!"

"I keep telling you" said a lady who was the ethnologist of the expedition "that the next great civilization will be a black civilization. The white man is played out. He knows it, too, and is committing suicide as fast as he can."

"Why are you surprised at a little thing like that?" said the black girl. "Why cannot you white people grow up and be serious as we blacks do? I thought glass beads marvellous when I saw them for the first time; but I soon got used to them. You cry marvellous every time one of you says something silly. The most wonderful things you have are your guns. It must be easier to find God than to find out how to make guns. But you do not care for God: you care for nothing but guns. You use your guns to make slaves of us. Then, because you are too lazy to shoot, you put the guns into our hands and teach us to shoot for you. You will soon teach us to make the guns because you are too lazy to make them yourselves. You have found out how to make drinks that make men forget God, and put their consciences to sleep and make murder seem a delight. You sell these drinks to us and teach us how to make them. And all the time you steal the land from us and starve us and make us hate you as we hate the snakes. What will be the end of that? You will kill one another so fast that those who are left will be too few to resist when our warriors fill themselves with your magic drink and kill you with your own guns. And then our warriors will kill one another as you do, unless they are prevented by God. Oh that I knew where I might find Him! Will none of you help me in my search? Do none of you care?"

"Our guns have saved you from the man-eating lion and the trampling elephant, have they not?" said a huffy gentleman, who had hitherto found the conversation too deep for him.

"Only to deliver us into the hands of the man-beating slave-driver and the trampling baas" said the black girl. "Lion and elephant shared the land with us. When they ate or trampled on our bodies they spared our souls. When they had enough they asked for no more. But nothing will satisfy your greed. You work generations of us to death until you have each of you more than a hundred of us could eat or spend; and yet you go on forcing us to work harder and harder and longer and longer for less and less food and clothing. You do not know what enough means for yourselves, or less than enough for us. You are for ever grumbling because we have no money to buy the goods you trade in; and your only remedy is to give us less money. This must be because you serve false gods. You are heathens and savages. You know neither how to live nor let others live. When I find God I shall have the strength of mind to destroy you and to teach my people not to destroy themselves."

"Look!" cried the first lady. "She is upsetting the men. I told you she would. They have been listening to her seditious rot. Look at their eyes. They are dangerous. I shall put a bullet through her if none of you men will."

And the lady actually drew a revolver, she was so frightened. But before she could get it out of its leather case the black girl sprang at her; laid her out with her favorite knobkerry stroke; and darted away into the forest. And all the black bearers went into ecstasies of merriment.

"Let us be thankful that she has restored good humor" said the first gentleman. "Things looked ugly for a moment. Now all is well. Doctor: will you see to poor Miss Fitzjones's cerebellum?"

"The mistake we made" said the naturalist "was in not offering her some of our food."

The black girl hid herself long enough to make sure that she was not being pursued. She knew that what she had done was a flogging matter, and that no plea of defence would avail a black defendant against a white plaintiff. She did not worry about the mounted police; for in that district they were very scarce. But she did not want to have to dodge the caravan continuously; and as one direction was as good as another for her purpose, she turned back on her tracks (for the caravan had been going her way) and so found herself towards evening at the well where she had talked with the conjurer. There she found a booth with many images of wood, plaster, or ivory set out for sale; and lying on the ground beside it was a big wooden cross on which the conjurer was lying with his ankles crossed and his arms stretched out. And the man who kept the booth was carving a statue of him in wood with great speed and skill. They were watched by a handsome Arab gentleman in a turban, with a scimitar in his sash, who was sitting on the coping of the well, and combing his beard.

"Why do you do this, my friend?" said the Arab gentleman. "You know that it is a breach of the second commandment given by God to Moses. By rights I should smite you dead with my scimitar; but I have suffered and sinned all my life through an infirmity of spirit which renders me incapable of slaying any animal, even a man, in cold blood. Why do you do it?"

"What else can I do if I am not to starve?" said the conjurer. "I am so utterly rejected of men that my only means of livelihood is to sit as a model to this compassionate artist who pays me sixpence an hour for stretching myself on this cross all day. He himself lives by selling images of me in this ridiculous position. People idolize me as the Dying Malefactor because they are interested in nothing but the police news. When he has laid in a sufficient stock of images, and I have saved a sufficient number of sixpences, I take a holiday and go about giving people good advice and telling them wholesome truths. If they would only listen to me they would be ever so much happier and better. But they refuse to believe me unless I do conjuring tricks for them; and when I do them they only throw me coppers and sometimes tickeys, and say what a wonderful man I am, and that there has been nobody like me ever on earth; but they go on being foolish and wicked and cruel all the same. It makes me feel that God has forsaken me sometimes."

"What is a tickey?" said the Arab, rearranging his robe in more becoming folds.

"A threepenny bit" said the conjurer. "It is coined because proud people are ashamed to be seen giving me coppers, and they think sixpence too much."

"I should not like people to treat me like that" said the Arab. "I also have a message to deliver. My people, if left to themselves, would fall down and worship all the images in that booth. If there were no images they would worship stones. My message

is that there is no majesty and no might save in Allah the glorious, the great, the one and only. Of Him no mortal has ever dared to make an image: if anyone attempted such a crime I should forget that Allah is merciful, and overcome my infirmity to the extremity of slaying him with my own hand. But who could conceive the greatness of Allah in a bodily form? Not even an image of the finest horse could convey a notion of His beauty and greatness. Well, when I tell them this, they ask me, too, to do conjuring tricks; and when I tell them that I am a man like themselves and that not Allah Himself can violate His own laws—if one could conceive Him as doing anything unlawful—they go away and pretend that I am working miracles. But they believe; for if they doubt I have them slain by those who believe. That is what you should do, my friend."

"But my message is that they should not kill one another" said the conjurer. "One has to be consistent."

"That is quite right as far as their private quarrels are concerned" said the Arab. "But we must kill those who are unfit to live. We must weed the garden as well as water it."

"Who is to be the judge of our fitness to live?" said the conjurer. "The highest authorities, the imperial governors, and the high priests, find that I am unfit to live. Perhaps they are right."

"Precisely the same conclusion was reached concerning myself" said the Arab. "I had to run away and hide until I had convinced a sufficient number of athletic young men that their elders were mistaken about me: that, in fact, the boot was on the other leg. Then I returned with the athletic young men, and weeded the garden."

"I admire your courage and practical sagacity" said the conjurer; "but I am not built that way."

"Do not admire such qualities" said the Arab. "I am somewhat ashamed of them. Every desert chieftain displays them abundantly. It is on the superiority of my mind, which has made me the vehicle of divine inspiration, that I value myself. Have you ever written a book?"

"No" said the conjurer sadly: "I wish I could; for then I could make money enough to come off this tiresome cross and send my message in print all over the world. But I am no author. I have composed a handy sort of short prayer with, I hope, all the essentials in it. But God inspires me to speak, not to write."

"Writing is useful" said the Arab. "I have been inspired to write many chapters of the word of Allah, praised be His name! But there are fellows in this world with whom Allah cannot be expected to trouble Himself. His word means nothing to them; so when I have to deal with them I am no longer inspired, and have to rely on my own invention and my own wit. For them I write terrible stories of the Day of Judgment, and of the hell in which evildoers will suffer eternally. I contrast these horrors with enchanting pictures of the paradise maintained for those who do the will of Allah. Such a paradise as will tempt them, you understand: a paradise of gardens and perfumes and beautiful women."

"And how do you know what is the will of Allah?" said the conjurer.

"As they are incapable of understanding it, my will must serve them for it instead" said the Arab. "They can understand my will, which is indeed truly the will of Allah at second hand, a little soiled by my mortal passions and necessities, no doubt, but the best I can do for them. Without it I could not manage them at all. Without it they would desert me for the first chief who promised them a bigger earthly plunder. But what other chief can write a book and promise them an eternity of bliss after their death with all the authority of a mind which can surround its own inventions with the majesty of authentic inspiration?"

"You have every qualification for success" said the conjurer politely, and a little wistfully.

"I am the eagle and the serpent" said the Arab. "Yet in my youth I was proud to be the servant of a widow and drive her camels. Now I am the humble servant of Allah and drive men for Him. For in no other do I recognize majesty and might; and with Him I take refuge from Satan and his brood."

"What is all this majesty and might without a sense of beauty and the skill to embody it in images that time cannot change into corruption?" said the wood carver, who had been working and listening in silence. "I have no use for your Allah, who forbids the making of images."

"Know, dog of an unbeliever" said the Arab, "that images have a power of making men fall down and worship them, even when they are images of beasts."

"Or of carpenters" interjected the conjurer.

"When I drove the camels" continued the Arab, not quite catching the interruption "I carried in my packs idols of men seated on thrones with the heads of hawks on their shoulders and scourges in their hands. The Christians who began by worshipping God in the form of a man, now worship him in the form of a lamb. This is the punishment decreed by Allah for the sin of presuming to imitate the work of His hands. But do not on that account dare to deny Allah his sense of beauty. Even your model here who is sharing your sin will remind you that the lilies of Allah are more lovely than the robes of Solomon in all his glory. Allah makes the skies His pictures and His children His statues, and does not withhold them from our earthy vision. He permits you to make lovely robes and saddles and trappings, and carpets to kneel on before Him, and windows like flower beds of precious stones. Yet you will be meddling in the work He reserves for Himself, and making idols. For ever be such sin forbidden to my people!"

"Pooh!" said the sculptor "your Allah is a bungler; and he knows it. I have in my booth in a curtained-off corner some Greek gods so beautiful that Allah himself may well burst with envy when he compares them with his own amateur attempts. I tell you Allah made this hand of mine because his own hands are too clumsy, if indeed he have any hands at all. The artist-god is himself an artist, never satisfied with His work, always perfecting it to the limit of His powers, always aware that though He must stop when He reaches that limit, yet there is a further perfection without which the picture has no meaning. Your Allah can make a woman. Can he make the Goddess of Love? No: only an artist can do that. See!" he said, rising to go into his booth. "Can Allah make *her*?" And he brought from the curtained corner a marble Venus and placed her on the counter.

"Her limbs are cold" said the black girl, who had been listening all this time unnoticed.

"Well said!" cried the Arab. "A living failure is better than a dead masterpiece; and Allah is justified against this most presumptuous idolater, whom I must have slain with a blow had you not slain him with a word."

"I still live" said the artist, unabashed. "That girl's limbs will one day be colder than any marble. Cut my goddess in two: she is still white marble to the core. Cut that girl in two with your scimitar, and see what you will find there."

"Your talk no longer interests me" said the Arab. "Maiden: there is yet room in my house for another wife. You are beautiful: your skin is like black satin: you are full of life."

"How many wives have you?" said the black girl.

"I have long since ceased to count them" replied the Arab; "but there are enough to shew you that I am an experienced husband and know how to make women as happy as Allah permits."

"I do not seek happiness: I seek God" said the black girl.

"Have you not found Him yet?" said the conjurer.

"I have found many gods" said the black girl. "Everyone I meet has one to offer me; and this image maker here has a whole shopful of them. But to me they are all half dead, except the ones that are half animals like this one on the top shelf, playing a mouth organ, who is half a goat and half a man. That is very true to nature; for I myself am half a goat and half a woman, though I should like to be a Goddess. But even these gods who are half goats are half men. Why are they never half women?"

"What about this one?" said the image maker, pointing to Venus.

"Why is her lower half hidden in a sack?" said the black girl. "She is neither a goddess nor a woman: she is ashamed of half her body, and the other half of her is what the white people call a lady. She is ladylike and beautiful; and a white Governor General would be glad to have her at the head of his house; but to my mind she has no conscience; and that makes her inhuman without making her godlike. I have no use for her."

"The Word shall be made flesh, not marble" said the conjurer. "You must not complain because these gods have the bodies of men. If they did not put on humanity for you, how could you, who are human, enter into any communion with them? To make a link between Godhood and Manhood, some god must become man."

"Or some woman become God" said the black girl. "That would be far better, because the god who condescends to be human degrades himself; but the woman who becomes God exalts herself."

"Allah be my refuge from all troublesome women" said the Arab. "This is the most troublesome woman I have ever met. It is one of the mysterious ways of Allah to make women troublesome when he makes them beautiful. The more reason he gives them to be content, the more dissatisfied they are. This one is dissatisfied even with Allah Himself, in whom is all majesty and all might. Well, maiden, since Allah the glorious and great cannot please you, what god or goddess can?"

"There is a goddess of whom I have heard, and of whom I

would know more" said the black girl. "She is named Myna; and I feel there is something about her that none of the other gods can give."

"There is no such goddess" said the image maker. "There are no other gods or goddesses except those I make; and I have never made a goddess named Myna."

"She most surely exists" said the black girl; "for the white missy spoke of her with reverence, and said that the key to the universe was the root of her womanhood and that it was bodiless like a number, and that it was before the beginning instead of after it, just as God was before creation. It is not Myna's sex but that which multiplied by itself makes Myna's sex. Something like that must have been the beginning; and something like that it must be that endures when we return to the dust out of which it made us. Since I was a child I have meditated on numbers and wondered how the number one came; for all the other numbers are only ones added to ones; but what I could not find out was what one is. But now I know through Myna that one is that which is multiplied by itself and not by a married pair. And when you have one you know why there is no beginning and no end; for you can count one less and less and less and never come to a beginning; and you can count one more and more and more and never come to an end: thus it is through numbers that you find eternity."

"Eternity in itself and by itself is nothing" said the Arab. "What is eternity to me if I cannot find eternal truth?"

"Only the truth of number is eternal" said the black girl. "Every other truth passes away or becomes error, like the fancies of our childhood; but one and one are two and one and ten eleven and always will be. Therefore I feel that there is something godlike about numbers."

"You cannot eat and drink numbers" said the image maker. "You cannot marry them."

"God has provided other things for us to eat and drink; and we can marry one another" said the black girl.

"Well, you cannot draw them; and that is enough for me" said the image maker.

"We Arabs can; and in this sign we shall conquer the world. See!" said the Arab. And he stooped and drew figures in the sand.

"The missionary says that God is a magic number that is three in one and one in three" said the black girl.

"That is simple" said the Arab; "for I am the son of my father and the father of my sons and myself to boot: three in one and one in three. Man's nature is manifold: Allah alone is one. He is unity. He is that which, as you say, is itself multiplied by itself. He is the core of the onion, the bodiless centre without which there could be no body. He is the number of the innumerable stars, the weight of the imponderable air, the—"

"You are a poet, I believe" said the image maker.

The Arab, thus interrupted, colored deeply; sprang to his feet; and drew his scimitar. "Do you dare accuse me of being a lewd balladmonger?" he said. "This is an insult to be wiped out in blood."

"Sorry" said the image maker. "I meant no offence. Why are you ashamed to make a ballad which outlives a thousand men, and not ashamed to make a corpse, which any fool can make, and which he has to hide in the earth when he has made it lest it stink him to death?"

"That is true" said the Arab, sheathing his weapon, and sitting down again. "It is one of the mysteries of Allah that when Satan makes impure verses Allah sends a divine tune to cleanse them. Nevertheless I was an honest cameldriver, and never took money for singing, though I confess I was much addicted to it."

"I too have not been righteous overmuch" said the conjurer. "I have been called a gluttonous man and a winebibber. I have not fasted. I have broken the sabbath. I have been kind to women who were no better than they should be. I have been unkind to my mother and shunned my family; for a man's true household is that in which God is the father and we are all his children, and not the belittling house and shop in which he must stay within reach of his mother's breast until he is weaned."

"A man needs many wives and a large household to prevent this cramping of his mind" said the Arab. "He should distribute his affection. Until he has known many women he cannot know the value of any; for value is a matter of comparison. I did not know what an old angel I had in my first wife until I found what a young devil I had in my last."

"And your wives?" said the black girl. "Are they also to know many men in order that they may learn your value?"

"I take refuge with Allah against this black daughter of Satan" cried the Arab vehemently. "Learn to hold your peace, woman, when men are talking and wisdom is their topic. God made Man before he made Woman."

"Second thoughts are best" said the black girl. "If it is as you say, God must have created Woman because He found Man insufficient. By what right do you demand fifty wives and condemn each of them to one husband?"

"Had I my life to live over again" said the Arab "I would be a celibate monk and shut my door upon women and their questions. But consider this. If I have only one wife I deny all other women any share in me, though many women will desire me in proportion to my excellence and their discernment. The enlightened woman who desires the best father for her children will ask for a fiftieth share in me rather than a piece of human refuse all to herself. Why should she suffer this injustice when there is no need for it?"

"How is she to know your value unless she has known fifty men to compare with you, seeing that value is a matter of comparison?" said the black girl.

"With Thee I take refuge, O Allah, who made men and women as they are" exclaimed the Arab despairingly. "What can I say except that the child who has fifty fathers has no father?"

"What matter if it have a mother?" said the black girl. "Besides, what you say is not true. One of the fifty will be its father."

"Know then" said the Arab "that there are many shameless women who have known men without number; but they do not bear children, whereas I, who covet and possess every desirable woman my eyes light on, have a large posterity. And from this it plainly appears that injustice to women is one of the mysteries of Allah, against whom it is vain to rebel. Allah is great and glorious; and in Him alone is there majesty and might; but His justice is beyond our understanding. My wives, who pamper themselves too much, bring forth their children in torments that wring my heart when I hear their cries; and these torments we men are spared. This is not just; but if you have no better remedy for such injustice than to let women do what men do and men do what women do, will you tell me to lie in and bear children? I can reply only that Allah will not have it so. It is against nature."

"I know that we cannot go against nature" said the black girl. "You cannot bear children; but a woman could have several husbands and could still bear children provided she had no more than one husband at a time."

"Among the other injustices of Allah" said the Arab "is his ordinance that a woman must have the last word. I am dumb."

"What happens" said the image maker "when fifty women assemble round one man, and each must have the last word?"

"The hell in which the one man expiates all his sins and takes refuge with Allah the merciful" said the Arab, with deep feeling.

"I shall not find God where men are talking about women" said the black girl, turning to go.

"Nor where women are talking about men" shouted the image maker after her.

She waved her hand in assent and left them. Nothing particular happened after that until she came to a prim little villa with a very amateurish garden which was being cultivated by a wizened old gentleman whose eyes were so striking that his face seemed all eyes, his nose so remarkable that his face seemed all

nose, and his mouth so expressive of a comically malicious relish that his face seemed all mouth until the black girl combined these three incompatibles by deciding that his face was all intelligence.

"Excuse me, baas" she said: "may I speak to you?"

"What do you want?" said the old gentleman.

"I want to ask my way to God" she said; "and as you have the most knowing face I have ever seen, I thought I would ask you."

"Come in" said he. "I have found, after a good deal of consideration, that the best place to seek God in is a garden. You can dig for Him there."

"That is not my idea of seeking for God at all" said the black girl, disappointed. "I will go on, thank you."

"Has your own idea, as you call it, led you to Him yet?"

"No" said the black girl, stopping: "I cannot say that it has. But I do not like your idea."

"Many people who have found God have not liked Him and have spent the rest of their lives running away from Him. Why do you suppose you would like Him?"

"I dont know" said the black girl. "But the missionary has a line of poetry that says that we needs must love the highest when we see it."

"That poet was a fool" said the old gentleman. "We hate it; we crucify it; we poison it with hemlock; we chain it to a stake and burn it alive. All my life I have striven in my little way to do God's work and teach His enemies to laugh at themselves; but if you told me God was coming down the road I should creep into the nearest mousehole and not dare to breathe until He had passed. For if He saw me or smelt me, might He not put His foot on me and squelch me, as I would squelch any venomous little thing that broke my commandments? These fellows who run after God crying 'Oh that I knew where I might find Him' must have a tremendous opinion of themselves to think that they could stand before him. Has the missionary ever told you the story of Jupiter and Semele?"

"No" said the black girl. "What is that story?"

"Jupiter is one of the names of God" said the old gentleman. "You know that He has many names, dont you?"

"The last man I met called him Allah" she said.

"Just so" said the old gentleman. "Well, Jupiter fell in love with Semele, and was considerate enough to appear and behave just like a man to her. But she thought herself good enough to be loved by a god in all the greatness of his godhood. So she insisted on his coming to her in the full panoply of his divinity."

"What happened when he did?" asked the black girl.

"Just what she might have known would happen if she had had any sense" said the old gentleman. "She shrivelled up and cracked like a flea in the fire. So take care. Do not be a fool like Semele. God is at your elbow, and He has been there all the time; but in His divine mercy He has not revealed Himself to you lest too full a knowledge of Him should drive you mad. Make a little garden for yourself: dig and plant and weed and prune; and be content if He jogs your elbow when you are gardening unskilfully, and blesses you when you are gardening well."

"And shall we never be able to bear His full presence?" said the black girl.

"I trust not" said the old philosopher. "For we shall never be able to bear His full presence until we have fulfilled all His purposes and become gods ourselves. But as His purposes are infinite, and we are most briefly finite, we shall never, thank God, be able to catch up with His purposes. So much the better for us. If our work were done we should be of no further use: that would be the end of us; for He would hardly keep us alive for the pleasure of looking at us, ugly and ephemeral insects as we are. Therefore come in and help to cultivate this garden to His glory. The rest you had better leave to Him."

So she laid down her knobkerry and went in and gardened with him. And from time to time other people came in and helped. At first this made the black girl jealous; but she hated feeling like that, and soon got used to their comings and goings.

One day she found a redhaired Irishman laboring in the back garden where they grew the kitchen stuff.

"Who let you in here?" she said.

"Faith, I let meself in" said the Irishman. "Why wouldnt I?"

"But the garden belongs to the old gentleman" said the black girl.

"I'm a Socialist" said the Irishman "and dont admit that gardens belongs to annybody. That oul' fella is cracked and past his work and needs somewan to dig his podatoes for him. There's a lot been found out about podatoes since he learnt to dig them."

"Then you did not come in to search for God?" said the black girl.

"Divvle a search" said the Irishman. "Sure God can search for me if He wants me. My own belief is that He's not all that He sets up to be. He's not properly made and finished yet. There's somethin in us that's dhrivin at Him, and somethin out of us that's dhrivin at Him: that's certain; and the only other thing that's certain is that the somethin makes plenty of mistakes in thryin to get there. We'v got to find out its way for it as best we can, you and I; for there's a hell of a lot of other people thinkin of nothin but their own bellies." And he spat on his hands and went on digging.

Both the black girl and the old gentleman thought the Irishman rather a coarse fellow (as indeed he was); but as he was useful and would not go away, they did their best to teach him nicer habits and refine his language. But nothing would ever persuade him that God was anything more solid and satisfactory than an eternal but as yet unfulfilled purpose, or that it could ever be fulfilled if the fulfilment were not made reasonably easy and hopeful by Socialism.

Still, when they had taught him manners and cleanliness they got used to him and even to his dreadful jokes. One day the old gentleman said to her "It is not right that a fine young woman like you should not have a husband and children. I am much too old for you; so you had better marry that Irishman."

As she had become very devoted to the old gentleman she was fearfully angry at first at his wanting her to marry anyone else, and even spent a whole night planning to drive the Irishman out of the place with her knobkerry. She could not bring herself to admit that the old gentleman had been born sixty years too early for her, and must in the course of nature die and leave her without a companion. But the old gentleman rubbed these flat facts into her so hard that at last she gave in; and the two went together into the kitchen garden and told the Irishman that she was going to marry him.

He snatched up his spade with a yell of dismay and made a dash for the garden gate. But the black girl had taken the precaution to lock it; and before he could climb it they overtook him and held him fast.

"Is it me marry a black heathen niggerwoman?" he cried piteously, forgetting all his lately acquired refinements of speech. "Lemme go, will yous. I dont want to marry annywan."

But the black girl held him in a grip of iron (softly padded, however); and the old gentleman pointed out to him that if he ran away he would only fall into the clutches of some strange woman who cared nothing about searching for God, and who would have a pale ashy skin instead of the shining black satin he was accustomed to. At last, after half an hour or so of argument and coaxing, and a glass of the old gentleman's best burgundy to encourage him, he said "Well, I dont mind if I do."

So they were married; and the black girl managed the Irishman and the children (who were charmingly coffee-colored) very capably, and even came to be quite fond of them. Between them and the garden and mending her husband's clothes (which she could not persuade him to leave off wearing) she was kept so busy that her search for God was crowded out of her head most of the time; but there were moments, especially when she was drying her favorite piccaninny, who was very docile and quiet, after his bath, in which her mind went back to her search;

only now she saw how funny it was that an unsettled girl should start off to pay God a visit, thinking herself the centre of the universe, and taught by the missionary to regard God as somebody Who had nothing better to do than to watch everything she did and worry Himself about her salvation. She even tickled the piccaninny and asked him "Suppose I had found God at home what should I have done when He hinted that I was staying too long and that He had other things to attend to?" It was a question which the piccaninny was quite unable to answer: he only chuckled hysterically and tried to grab her wrists. It was only when the piccaninnies grew up and became independent of her, and the Irishman had become an unconscious habit of hers, as if he were a part of herself, that they ceased to take her away from herself and she was left once more with the leisure and loneliness that threw her back on such questions. And by that time her strengthened mind had taken her far beyond the stage at which there is any fun in smashing idols with knobkerries.

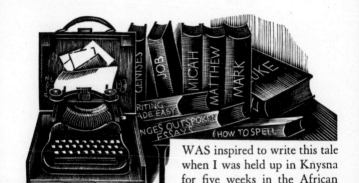

WAS inspired to write this tale when I was held up in Knysna for five weeks in the African summer and English winter of 1932. My intention was to write a play in the ordinary course of my business as a playwright; but I found myself writing the story of the black girl instead. And now, the story being written, I proceed to speculate on what it means, though I cannot too often repeat that I am as liable as anyone else to err in my interpretation, and that pioneer writers, like other pioneers, often mistake their destination as Columbus did. That is how they sometimes run away in pious horror from the conclusions to which their revelations manifestly lead. I hold, as firmly as St Thomas Aquinas, that all truths, ancient or modern, are divinely inspired; but I know by observation and introspection that the instrument on which the inspiring force plays may be a very faulty one, and may even end, like Bunyan in The Holy War, by making the most ridiculous nonsense of his message.

However, here is my own account of the matter for what it is worth.

It is often said, by the heedless, that we are a conservative species, impervious to new ideas. I have not found it so. I am often appalled at the avidity and credulity with which new ideas are snatched at and adopted without a scrap of sound evidence. People will believe anything that amuses them, gratifies them, or promises them some sort of profit. I console myself, as Stuart Mill did, with the notion that in time the silly ideas will lose their charm and drop out of fashion and out of existence; that the false promises, when broken, will pass through cynical derision into oblivion; and that after this sifting process the sound ideas, being indestructible (for even if suppressed or forgotten they are rediscovered again and again) will survive and be added to the body of ascertained knowledge we call Science. In this way we acquire a well tested stock of ideas to furnish our minds, such furnishing being education proper as distinguished from the pseudo-education of the schools and universities.

Unfortunately there is a snag in this simple scheme. It forgets the prudent old precept, "Dont throw out your dirty water until you get in your clean" which is the very devil unless completed by "This also I say unto you, that when you get your fresh water you must throw out the dirty, and be particularly careful not to let the two get mixed."

Now this is just what we never do. We persist in pouring the clean water into the dirty; and our minds are always muddled in consequence. The educated human of today has a mind which can be compared only to a store in which the very latest and most precious acquisitions are flung on top of a noisome heap of rag-and-bottle refuse and worthless antiquities from the museum lumber room. The store is always bankrupt; and the men in possession include William the Conqueror and Henry the Seventh, Moses and Jesus, St Augustine and Sir Isaac Newton, Calvin and Wesley, Queen Victoria and Mr H. G. Wells; whilst among the distraining creditors are Karl Marx, Einstein, and dozens of people more or less like Stuart Mill and myself. No mind can operate reasonably in such a mess. And as our current schooling and colleging and graduating consists in reproducing this mess in the minds of every fresh generation of children, we are provoking revolutionary emergencies in which persons muddled by university degrees will have to be politically disfranchised and disqualified as, in effect, certified lunatics, and the direction of affairs given over to the self-educated and the simpletons.

The most conspicuous example of this insane practice of continually taking in new ideas without ever clearing out the ideas they supersede, is the standing of the Bible in those countries in which the extraordinary artistic value of the English translation has given it a magical power over its readers. That power is now waning because, as sixteenth century English is a dying tongue, new translations are being forced on us by the plain fact that the old one is no longer intelligible to the masses. These new versions have—the good ones by their admirable homeliness and the ordinary ones by their newspapery everydayness—suddenly placed the Bible narratives in a light of familiar realism which obliges their readers to apply common sense tests to them.

But the influence of these modern versions is not yet very

wide. It seems to me that those who find the old version unintelligible and boresome do not resort to modern versions: they simply give up reading the Bible. The few who are caught and interested by the new versions, stumble on them by accidents which, being accidents, are necessarily rare. But they still hear Lessons read in church in the old version in a specially reverent tone; children at Sunday School are made to learn its verses by heart, and are rewarded by little cards inscribed with its texts; and bedrooms and nurseries are still decorated with its precepts, warnings, and consolations. The British and Foreign Bible Society has distributed more than three million copies annually for a century past; and though many of these copies may be mere churchgoers' luggage, never opened on weekdays, or gifts in discharge of the duties of godparents; yet they count. There is still on the statute book a law which no statesman dare repeal, which makes it felony to question the scientific truth and supernatural authority of any word of Holy Scripture, the penalties extending to ruinous outlawry; and the same acceptance of the Bible as an infallible encyclopedia is one of the Articles of the Church of England, though another Article, and that the very first, flatly denies the corporeal and voracious nature of God insisted on in the Pentateuch.

In all these instances the Bible means the translation authorized by King James the First of the best examples in ancient Jewish literature of natural and political history, of poetry, morality, theology, and rhapsody. The translation was extraordinarily well done because to the translators what they were translating was not merely a curious collection of ancient books written by different authors in different stages of culture, but the Word of God divinely revealed through his chosen and expressly inspired scribes. In this conviction they carried out their work with boundless reverence and care and achieved a beautifully artistic result. It did not seem possible to them that they could flatter the original texts; for who could improve on God's own style? And as they could not conceive that divine revelation could conflict with what they believed to be the truths of their religion, they did not hesitate to translate a negative by a positive where such a conflict seemed to arise, as they could hardly trust their own fallible knowledge of ancient Hebrew when it contradicted the very foundations of their faith, nor doubt that God would, as they prayed Him to do, take care that his message should not suffer corruption in their hands. In this state of exaltation they made a translation so magnificent that to this day the common human Britisher or citizen of the United States of North America accepts and worships it as a single book by a single author, the book being the Book of Books and the author being God. Its charm, its promise of salvation, its pathos, and its majesty have been raised to transcendence by Handel, who can still make atheists cry and give materialists the thrill of the sublime with his Messiah. Even the ignorant, to whom religion is crude fetishism and magic, prize it as a paper talisman that will exorcise ghosts, prevent witnesses from lying, and, if carried devoutly in a soldier's pocket, stop bullets.

Now it is clear that this supernatural view of the Bible, though at its best it may achieve sublimity by keeping its head in the skies, may also make itself both ridiculous and dangerous by having its feet off the ground. It is a matter of daily experience that a book taken as an infallible revelation, whether the author be Moses, Ezekiel, Paul, Swedenborg, Joseph Smith, Mary Baker Eddy, or Karl Marx, may bring such hope, consolation, interest and happiness into our individual lives that we may well cherish it as the key of Paradise. But if the paradise be a fool's paradise, as it must be when its materials are imaginary, then it must not be made the foundation of a State, and must be classed with anodynes, opiates, and anæsthetics. It is not for nothing that the fanatically religious leaders of the new Russia dismissed the religion of the Greek Church as "dope." That is precisely what a religion becomes when it is divorced from reality. It is useful to ambitious rulers in corrupt political systems as a sedative to popular turbulence (that is why the tyrant always makes much of the priest); but in the long run civilization must get back to honest reality or perish.

At present we are at a crisis in which one party is keeping the Bible in the clouds in the name of religion, and another is trying to get rid of it altogether in the name of Science. Both names are so recklessly taken in vain that the Bishop of Birmingham has just warned his flock that the scientific party is drawing nearer to Christ than the Church congregations. I, who am a sort of unofficial Bishop of Everywhere, have repeatedly warned the scientists that the Quakers are fundamentally far more scientific than the official biologists. In this confusion I venture to suggest that we neither leave the Bible in the clouds nor attempt the impossible task of suppressing it. Why not simply bring it down to the ground, and take it for what it really is?

To maintain good humor I am quite willing to concede to my Protestant friends that the Bible in the clouds was sometimes turned to good account in the struggles to maintain Protestant Freethought (such as it was) against the Churches and Empires. The soldier who had his Bible in one hand and his weapon in the other fought with the strength of ten under Cromwell, William of Orange, and Gustavus Adolphus. The very old-fashioned may still permit themselves a little romance about the Ironsides at Dunbar singing "O God, our help in ages past," about the ships that broke the boom and relieved the siege of Londonderry, and even about Dugald Dalgetty. But the struggle between Guelph and Ghibelline is so completely over that in its last and bloodiest war the ministers of the Guelph king did not even know what his name meant, and made him discard it in the face of the Ghibelline Kaiser and the Holy Roman Empire. And the soldier fought with the trigger of a machine gun in one hand and a popular newspaper in the other. Thanks to the machine gun he fought with the strength of a thousand; but the idolized Bible was still at the back of the popular newspaper, full of the spirit of the campaigns of Joshua, holding up our sword as the sword of the Lord and Gideon, and hounding us on to the slaughter of those modern Amalekites and Canaanites, the Germans, as idolators, and children of the devil. Though the formula (King and Country) was different, the spirit was the same: it was the old imaginary conflict of Jehovah against Baal; only, as the Germans were also fighting for King and Country, and were quite as convinced as we that Jehovah, the Lord strong and mighty, the Lord mighty in battle, the Lord of Hosts (now called big battalions), was their God, and that ours was his enemy, the fighting, though fearfully slaughterous, was so completely neutralized that the victory had to be won by blockade. But the wounds to civilization were so serious that we do not as yet know whether they are not going to prove mortal, because they are being kept open by the Old Testament spirit and methods and superstitions. And here again it is important to notice that the only country which seems to be vigorously recovering is Russia, which has thrown the Old Testament violently and contemptuously into the waste paper basket, and even, in the intensity of its reaction against it, organized its children into a League of the Godless, thereby unexpectedly suffering them to obey the invitation of Jesus to come unto him, whilst we are organizing our children in Officers' Training Corps: a very notable confirmation of the Bishop of Birmingham's observation that scientific atheism moves towards Christ whilst official Christianity pulls savagely in the opposite direction.

The situation is past trifling. The ancient worshippers of Jehovah, armed with sword and spear, and demoralized by a clever boy with a sling, could not murder and destroy wholesale. But with machine gun and amphibious tank, aeroplane and gas bomb, operating on cities where millions of inhabitants are depending for light and heat, water and food, on centralized mechanical organs like great steel hearts and arteries, that can be smashed in half an hour by a boy in a bomber, we really must take care that the boy is better educated than Noah and Joshua.

In plain words, as we cannot get rid of the Bible, it will get rid of us unless we learn to read it "in the proper spirit," which I take to be the spirit of intellectual integrity that obliges honest thinkers to read every line which pretends to divine authority with all their wits about them, and to judge it exactly as they judge the Koran, the Upanishads, the Arabian Nights, this morning's leading article in *The Times,* or last week's cartoon in *Punch,* knowing that all written words are equally open to inspiration from the eternal fount and equally subject to error from the mortal imperfection of their authors.

Then say, of what use is the Bible nowadays to anyone but the antiquary and the literary connoisseur? Why not boot it into the dustbin as the Soviet has done? Well, there is a *prima facie* case to be made out for that. Let us first do justice to it.

What about the tables of the law? the ten commandments? They did not suffice even for the wandering desert tribe upon whom they were imposed by Moses, who, like Mahomet later on, could get them respected only by pretending that they were supernaturally revealed to him. They had to be supplemented by the elaborate codes of Leviticus and Deuteronomy, which the most fanatically observant Jew could not now obey without outraging our modern morality and violating our criminal law. They are mere lumber nowadays; for their simpler validities are the necessary commonplaces of human society and need no Bible to reveal them or give them authority. The second commandment, taken to heart by Islam, is broken and ignored throughout Christendom, though its warning against the enchantments of fine art is worthy the deepest consideration, and, had its author known the magic of word-music as he knew that of the graven image, might stand as a warning against our idolatry of the Bible. The whole ten are unsuited and inadequate to modern needs, as they say not a word against those forms of robbery, legalized by the robbers, which have uprooted the moral foundation of our society and will condemn us to slow social decay if we are not wakened up, as Russia has been, by a crashing collapse.

In addition to these negative drawbacks there is the positive one that the religion inculcated in the earlier books is a crudely atrocious ritual of human sacrifice to propitiate a murderous tribal deity who was, for example, induced to spare the human race from destruction in a second deluge by the pleasure given him by the smell of burning flesh when Noah "took of every clean beast and of every clean fowl, and offered burnt offerings on the altar." And though this ritual is in the later books fiercely repudiated, and its god denied in express terms, by the prophet Micah, shewing how it was outgrown as the Jews progressed in culture, yet the tradition of a blood sacrifice whereby the vengeance of a terribly angry god can be bought off by a vicarious and hideously cruel blood sacrifice persists even through the New Testament, where it attaches itself to the torture and execution of Jesus by the Roman governor of Jerusalem, idolizing that horror in Noah's fashion as a means by which we can all cheat our consciences, evade our moral responsibilities, and turn our shame into self-congratulation by loading all our infamies on to the scourged shoulders of Christ. It would be hard to imagine a more demoralizing and unchristian doctrine:

indeed it would not be at all unreasonable for the Intellectual Co-operation Committee of the League of Nations to follow the example of the Roman Catholic Church by objecting to the promiscuous circulation of the Bible (except under conditions amounting to careful spiritual direction) until the supernatural claims made for its authority are finally and unequivocally dropped.

As to Bible science, it has over the nineteenth-century materialistic fashion in biology the advantage of being a science of life and not an attempt to substitute physics and chemistry for it; but it is hopelessly pre-evolutionary; its descriptions of the origin of life and morals are obviously fairy tales; its astronomy is terracentric; its notions of the starry universe are childish; its history is epical and legendary: in short, people whose education in these departments is derived from the Bible are so absurdly misinformed as to be unfit for public employment, parental responsibility, or the franchise. As an encyclopedia, therefore, the Bible must be shelved with the first edition of the Encyclopedia Britannica as a record of what men once believed, and a measure of how far they have left their obsolete beliefs behind.

Granted all this to Russia, it does not by any means dispose of the Bible. A great deal of the Bible is much more alive than this morning's paper and last night's parliamentary debate. Its chronicles are better reading than most of our fashionable histories, and less intentionally mendacious. In revolutionary invective and Utopian aspiration it cuts the ground from under the feet of Ruskin, Carlyle, and Karl Marx; and in epics of great leaders and great rascals it makes Homer seem superficial and Shakespear unbalanced. And its one great love poem is the only one that can satisfy a man who is really in love. Shelley's Epipsychidion is, in comparison, literary gas and gaiters.

In sum, it is an epitome, illustrated with the most stirring examples, of the history of a tribe of mentally vigorous, imaginative, aggressively acquisitive humans who developed into a nation through ruthless conquest, encouraged by the delusion that they were "the chosen people of God" and, as such, the natural inheritors of all the earth, with a reversion to a blissful eternity hereafter in the kingdom of heaven. And the epitome in no way suppresses the fact that this delusion led at last to their dispersion, denationalization, and bigoted persecution by better disciplined states which, though equally confident of a monopoly of divine favor earned by their own merits, paid the Jews the compliment of adopting the Hebrew gods and prophets, as, on the whole, more useful to imperialist rulers than the available alternatives.

Now the difference between an illiterate savage and a person who has read such an epitome (with due skipping of its genealogical rubbish and the occasional nonsenses produced by attempts to translate from imperfectly understood tongues) is enormous. A community on which such a historical curriculum is imposed in family and school may be more dangerous to its neighbors, and in greater peril of collapse from intolerance and megalomania, than a community that reads either nothing or silly novels, football results, and city articles; but it is beyond all question a more highly educated one. It is therefore not in

the least surprising nor unreasonable that when the only gen-
erally available alternative to Bible education is no liberal education at all, many who have no illusions about the Bible, and
fully comprehend its drawbacks, vote for Bible education *faute
de mieux*. This is why mere criticism of Bible education cuts
so little ice. Ancient Hebrew history and literature, half fabulous
as it is, is better than no history and no literature; and I neither
regret nor resent my own Bible education, especially as my
mind soon grew strong enough to take it at its real value. At
worst the Bible gives a child a better start in life than the gutter.

This testimonial will please our Bible idolators; but it must
not for a moment soothe them into believing that their fetichism
can now be defended by the plea that it was better to be Noah
or Abraham or Sir Isaac Newton than a London street arab.
Street arabs are not very common in these days of compulsory
attendance at the public elementary school. The alternative to
the book of Genesis at present is not mere ignorant nescience,
but Mr H. G. Wells's Outline of History, and the host of imita-
tions and supplements which its huge success has called into
existence. Within the last two hundred years a body of history,
literature, poetry, science, and art has been inspired and created
by precisely the same mysterious impulse that inspired and
created the Bible. In all these departments it leaves the Bible
just nowhere. It is the Bible-educated human who is now the
ignoramus. If you doubt it, try to pass an examination for any
practical employment by giving Bible answers to the examiners'
questions. You will be fortunate if you are merely plucked and
not certified as a lunatic. Throughout the whole range of

Science which the Bible was formerly supposed to cover with an infallible authority, it is now hopelessly superseded, with one exception. That exception is the science of theology, which is still so completely off the ground—so metaphysical, as the learned say—that our materialist scientists contemptuously deny it the right to call itself science at all.

But there is no surer symptom of a sordid and fundamentally stupid mind, however powerful it may be in many practical activities, than a contempt for metaphysics. A person may be supremely able as a mathematician, engineer, parliamentary tactician or racing bookmaker; but if that person has contemplated the universe all through life without ever asking "What the devil does it all mean?" he (or she) is one of those people for whom Calvin accounted by placing them in his category of the predestinately damned.

Hence the Bible, scientifically obsolete in all other respects, remains interesting as a record of how the idea of God, which is the first effort of civilized mankind to account for the existence and origin and purpose of as much of the universe as we are conscious of, develops from a childish idolatry of a thundering, earthquaking, famine striking, pestilence launching, blinding, deafening, killing, destructively omnipotent Bogey Man, maker of night and day and sun and moon, of the four seasons and their miracles of seed and harvest, to a braver idealization of a benevolent sage, a just judge, an affectionate father, evolving finally into the incorporeal word that never becomes flesh, at which point modern science and philosophy takes up the problem with its *Vis Naturæ,* its *Élan Vital,* its Life Force, its

Evolutionary Appetite, its still more abstract Categorical Imperative, and what not?

Now the study of this history of the development of a hypothesis from savage idolatry to a highly cultivated metaphysic is as interesting, instructive, and reassuring as any study can be to an open mind and an honest intellect. But we spoil it all by that lazy and sluttish practice of not throwing out the dirty water when we get in the clean. The Bible presents us with a succession of gods, each being a striking improvement on the previous one, marking an Ascent of Man to a nobler and deeper conception of Nature, every step involving a purification of the water of life and calling for a thorough emptying and cleansing of the vessel before its replenishment by a fresh and cleaner supply. But we baffle the blessing by just sloshing the water from the new fountain into the contents of the dirty old bucket, and repeat this folly until our minds are in such a filthy mess that we are objects of pity to the superficial but clear-headed atheists who are content without metaphysics and can see nothing in the whole business but its confusions and absurdities. Practical men of business refuse to be bothered with such crazy matters at all.

Take the situation in detail as it develops through the Bible. The God of Noah is not the God of Job. Contemplate first the angry deity who drowned every living thing on earth, except one family of each species, in a fit of raging disgust at their wickedness, and then allowed the head of the one human family to appease him by "the sweet savour" of a heap of burning flesh! Is he identical with the tolerant, argumentative, academic, urbane, philosophic speculator who entertained the devil familiarly and made a wager with him that he could not drive Job to despair of divine benevolence? People who cannot see the difference between these two Gods cannot pass the most elementary test of intelligence: they cannot distinguish between similars and dissimilars.

But though Job's God is a great advance on Noah's God, he is a very bad debater, unless indeed we give him credit for deliberately saving himself from defeat by the old expedient: "No case: abuse the plaintiff's attorney." Job having raised the problem of the existence of evil and its incompatibility with omnipotent benevolence, it is no valid reply to jeer at him for being unable to create a whale or to play with it as with a bird. And there is a very suspicious touch of Noah's God in the offer to overlook the complicity of Job's friends in his doubts in consideration of a sacrifice of seven bullocks and seven rams. God's attempt at an argument is only a repetition and elaboration of the sneers of Elihu, and is so abruptly tacked on to them that one concludes that it must be a pious forgery to conceal the fact that the original poem left the problem of evil unsolved and Job's criticism unanswered, as indeed it remained until Creative Evolution solved it.

When we come to Micah we find him throwing out the dirty water fearlessly. He will not have Noah's God, nor even Job's God with his seven bullocks and seven rams. He raises the conception of God to the highest point it has ever attained by his fiercely contemptuous denunciation of the blood sacrifices, and his inspired and inspiring demand "What doth the Lord require of thee but to do justly, and to love mercy, and to walk humbly with thy God?" Before this victory of the human spirit over crude superstition Noah's God and Job's God go down like skittles: there is an end of them. And yet our children are taught, not to exult in this great triumph of spiritual insight over mere animal terror of the Bogey Man, but to believe that Micah's God and Job's God and Noah's God are one and the same, and that every good child must revere the spirit of justice and mercy and humility equally with the appetite for burnt flesh and human sacrifice, such indiscriminate and nonsensical reverence being inculcated as religion.

Later on comes Jesus, who dares a further flight. He suggests that godhead is something which incorporates itself in man: in himself, for instance. He is immediately stoned by his horrified hearers, who can see nothing in the suggestion but a monstrous attempt on his part to impersonate Jehovah. This misunderstanding, typical of dirty water theology, was made an article of religion eighteen hundred years later by Emanuel Swedenborg. But the unadulterated suggestion of Jesus is an advance on the theology of Micah; for Man walking humbly before an external God is an ineffective creature compared to Man exploring as the instrument and embodiment of God with no other guide than the spark of divinity within him. It is certainly the greatest break in the Bible between the Old and the New Testament. Yet the dirty water still spoils it; for we find Paul holding up Christ to the Ephesians as "an offering and a sacrifice to God for a sweet smelling savour," thereby dragging Christianity back and down to the level of Noah. None of the apostles rose above that level; and the result was that the great advances made by Micah and Jesus were cancelled; and historical Christianity was built up on the sacrificial altars of Jehovah, with Jesus as the sacrifice. What he and Micah would say if they could return and see their names and credit attached to the idolatries they abhorred can be imagined only by those who understand and sympathize with them.

Jesus could be reproached for having chosen his disciples very unwisely if we could believe that he had any real choice. There are moments when one is tempted to say that there was not one Christian among them, and that Judas was the only one who shewed any gleams of common sense. Because Jesus had mental powers and insight quite beyond their comprehension they worshipped him as a superhuman and indeed supernatural phenomenon, and made his memory the nucleus of their crude belief in magic, their Noahism, their sentimentality, their masochist Puritanism, and their simple morality with its punitive sanctions, decent and honest and amiable enough, some of it, but never for a moment on the intellectual level of Jesus, and at worst pregnant with all the horrors of the later wars of religion, the Jew burnings of Torquemada, and the atrocities of which all the pseudo-Christian Churches were guilty the moment they became powerful enough to persecute.

Most unfortunately the death of Jesus helped to vulgarize his reputation and obscure his doctrine. The Romans, though they executed their own political criminals by throwing them from the Tarpeian rock, punished slave revolts by crucifixion. They crucified six thousand of the followers of the revolutionary gladiator, Spartacus, a century before Jesus was denounced to them by the Jewish high priest as an agitator of the same kidney. He was accordingly tortured and killed in this hideous manner, with the infinitely more hideous result that the cross and the other instruments of his torture were made the symbols of the faith legally established in his name three hundred years later. They are still accepted as such throughout Christendom. The crucifixion thus became to the Churches what the Chamber of Horrors is to a waxwork: the irresistible attraction for children and for the crudest adult worshippers. Christ's clean water of life is befouled by the dirtiest of dirty water from the idolatries of his savage forefathers; and our prelates and proconsuls take Caiaphas and Pontius Pilate for their models in the name of their despised and rejected victim.

The case was further complicated by the pitiable fact that Jesus himself, shaken by the despair which unsettled the reason of Swift and Ruskin and many others at the spectacle of human cruelty, injustice, misery, folly, and apparently hopeless political incapacity, and perhaps also by the worship of his disciples and of the multitude, had allowed Peter to persuade him that he was the Messiah, and that death could not prevail against him nor prevent his returning to judge the world and establish his reign on earth for ever and ever. As this delusion came as easily within the mental range of his disciples as his social doctrine had been far over their heads, "Crosstianity" became established on the authority of Jesus himself. Later on, in a curious record of the visions of a drug addict which was absurdly admitted to the canon under the title of Revelation, a thousand years were specified as the period that was to elapse before Jesus was to return as he had promised. In 1000 A.D. the last possibility of the promised advent expired; but by that time people were so used to the delay that they readily substituted for the Second Advent a Second Postponement. Pseudo-Christianity was, and always will be, fact proof.

The whole business is an amazing muddle, which has held out not only because the views of Jesus were above the heads of all but the best minds, but because his appearance was followed by the relapse in civilization which we call the Dark Ages, from which we are only just emerging sufficiently to begin to pick up the thread of Christ's most advanced thought and rescue it from the mess the apostles and their successors made of it.

Six hundred years after Jesus, Mahomet founded Islam and made a colossal stride ahead from mere stock-and-stone idolatry to a very enlightened Unitarianism; but though he died a conqueror, and therefore escaped being made the chief attraction in an Arabian Chamber of Horrors, he found it impossible to control his Arabs without enticing and intimidating them by promises of a delightful life for the faithful, and threats of an eternity of disgusting torment for the wicked, after their bodily death, and also, after some honest protests, by accepting the supernatural character thrust on him by the childish superstition of his followers; so that he, too, now needs to be rediscovered in his true nature before Islam can come back to earth as a living faith.

And now I think the adventures of the black girl as revealed to me need no longer puzzle anyone. They could hardly have

happened to a white girl steeped from her birth in the pseudo-Christianity of the Churches. I take it that the missionary lifted her straight out of her native tribal fetichism into an unbiassed contemplation of the Bible with its series of gods marking stages in the development of the conception of God from the monster Bogey Man to the Father; then to the spirit without body, parts, nor passions; and finally to the definition of that spirit in the words God is Love. For the primitive two her knobkerry suffices; but when she reaches the end she has to point out that Love is not enough (like Edith Cavell making the same discovery about Patriotism) and that it is wiser to take Voltaire's advice by cultivating her garden and bringing up her piccaninnies than to spend her life imagining that she can find a complete explanation of the universe by laying about her with a knobkerry.

Still, the knobkerry has to be used as far as the way is clear.

Mere agnosticism leads nowhere. When the question of the existence of Noah's idol is raised on the point, vital to high civilization, whether our children shall continue to be brought up to worship it and compound for their sins by sacrificing to it, or, more cheaply, by sheltering themselves behind another's sacrifice to it, then whoever hesitates to bring down the knob-kerry with might and main is ludicrously unfit to have any part in the government of a modern State. The importance of a message to that effect at the present world crisis is probably at the bottom of my curious and sudden inspiration to write this tale instead of cumbering theatrical literature with another stage comedy.

AYOT ST LAWRENCE,
    9th October 1932.